GRAPHIC EXPEDITIONS

RESCUE IN ANTARCTICA

AN *Isabel Soto* GEOGRAPHY ADVENTURE

Emily Sohn

illustrated by Steven Butler and Anne Timmons

www.raintreepublishers.co.uk
Visit our website to find out
more information about
Raintree books.

Phone 0845 6044371
Fax +44 (0) 1865 312263
Email myorders@capstonepub.co.uk

Customers from outside the UK please telephone +44 1865 312262

Raintree is an imprint of Capstone Global Library Limited, a company incorporated in England and
Wales having its registered office at 7 Pilgrim Street, London EC4V 6LB
Registered company number: 6695882

"Raintree" is a registered trademark of Pearson Education Limited, under licence to Capstone Global
Library Limited

Text © Capstone Press 2010
First published by Capstone Press in 2010
First published in hardback in the United Kingdom by Capstone Global Library in 2010
The moral rights of the proprietor have been asserted.

British Library Cataloguing in Publication Data
Sohn, Emily -- Rescue in Antarctica: an Isabel Soto geography adventure
A full catalogue record for this book is available from the British Library.

ISBN 978 1 406 21443 7 (hardback)
14 13 12 11 10
10 9 8 7 6 5 4 3 2 1

Art Director and Designer: Alison Thiele
Cover Artist: Tod Smith
Colourist: Krista Ward
UK Editor: Diyan Leake
UK Production: Victoria Fitzgerald
Originated by Capstone Global Library
Printed and bound in China by South China Printing Company Limited

Photo credits: DigitalVision p. 7 (Getty Images); Getty Images Inc. p. 23
(Riser/Paul Souders).

Design elements: Shutterstock/Chen Ping Hung (framed edge design); mmmm (world
map design); Mushakesa (abstract lines design); Najin (old parchment design)

CONTENTS

Somewhere in the Sahara desert, 1750

Ancient desert cultures are fascinating. It's amazing how the native people can survive in such a hot and dry climate.

The village is empty, but this fire pit is still smouldering. I wonder where everyone went?

BZZZT! BZZZ!

That's strange. I wasn't expecting a call from Tom Baker.

Isabel! Thank goodness I've reached you. Greg and Sheila are missing in Antarctica.

Missing! How?

Come back to the museum and I'll give you the details.

I'll be there as soon as I can.

THE COLD FACTS

- Antarctica is about 1.3 times the size of Europe.
- The highest mountain in Antarctica is more than 4,877 metres (16,000 feet) tall.
- The coldest temperature ever recorded on earth was in Antarctica. It was a bone-chilling minus 89 degrees Celsius (minus 129 degrees Fahrenheit).
- Antarctica contains 90 percent of the world's ice.

9

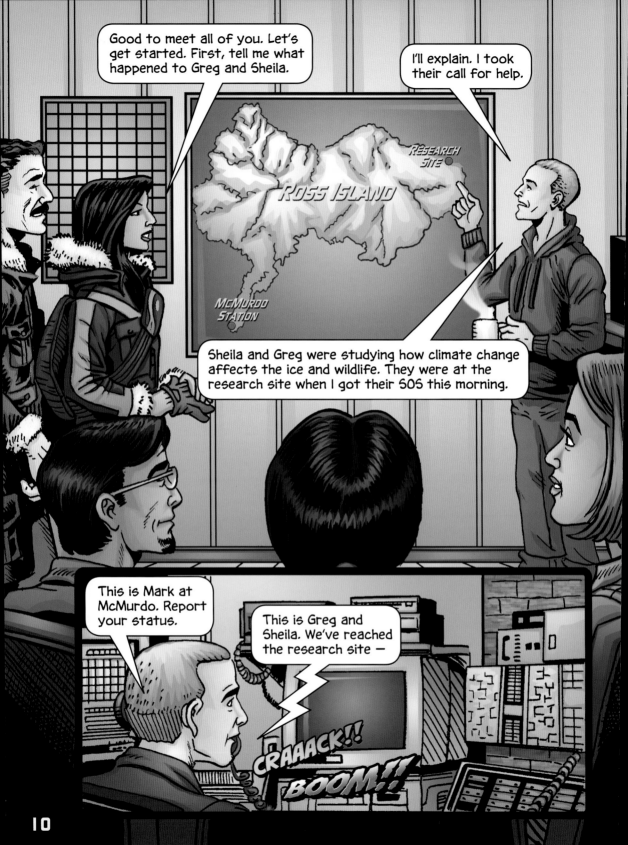

ICEBERG

RESEARCH SITE

ROSS ISLAND

McMURDO STATION

WEDDELL SEA

ROSS SEA

ANTARCTIC COASTAL CURRENT (EAST WIND DRIFT)

ANTARCTICA

ANTARCTIC CIRCUMPOLAR CURRENT (WEST WIND DRIFT)

We need to find that drifting iceberg. What direction do you think it's headed?

Near the coast, water moves in an anticlockwise direction. If the iceberg is still close to land, it's probably drifting westward.

ANTARCTIC OCEAN CURRENTS

The Southern Ocean connects the Atlantic, Pacific, and Indian Oceans. The Antarctic Coastal Current flows anticlockwise near the coast. Further out to sea, winds push the Antarctic Circumpolar Current in a clockwise direction.

McMurdo Station, 5.30 in the morning

Good morning, Isabel. Did you sleep well?

Yes, but sleeping while the sun is still up was strange.

You get used to it after a while. We're just getting our survival gear together. Conditions can become dangerous very quickly in Antarctica. We need to be prepared.

On 5 December 1914, the British explorer Ernest Shackleton and his crew sailed toward Antarctica on the *Endurance*. Shackleton wanted to be the first person to cross Antarctica on foot.

But the *Endurance* never made it to land. The ship got stuck in the ice in the Weddell Sea. On 21 November 1915, the *Endurance* was crushed by sea ice and sank.

Shackleton and his crew managed to save three small lifeboats. But the sea was frozen. They had to drag the boats across the ice. After a few days, they had only travelled a few miles. They decided to set up a camp and wait for the ice to break apart.

On 9 April 1916, the ice broke, allowing the crew to row the boats. Eventually, they made it to Elephant Island. But there was no hope for rescue. Luckily, the crew had enough supplies to set up a survival camp.

Shackleton soon made a risky decision. On 24 April 1916, he took five men and sailed a lifeboat hundreds of miles to South Georgia Island. The journey took 17 days.

The small group then hiked more than 32 kilometres, or 20 miles, over the mountains to the other side of the island. They finally found help at a whaling station.

That summer, Shackleton made three attempts to rescue his crew. But the ships had to turn back each time. Finally, on 30 August 1916, the *Yelcho* arrived at Elephant Island.

Shackleton's men were finally saved. They had spent 22 long months at sea. But they all lived to tell of their adventures.

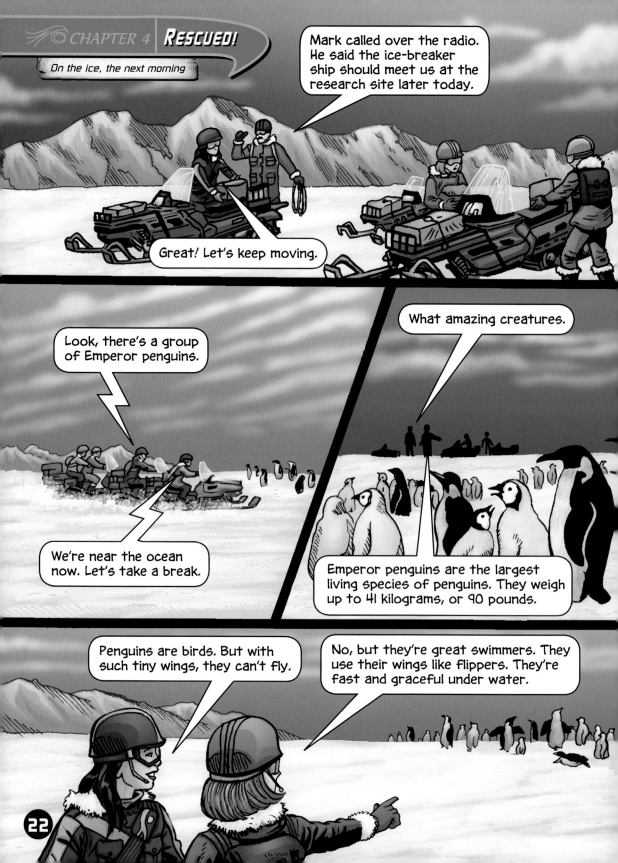

For the babies

After laying an egg, female Emperor penguins travel up to 80 kilometres (50 miles) to find food in open water. While the mothers are gone, the fathers protect the eggs. They keep the eggs warm by holding them on their feet until the chicks hatch. The fathers don't eat until the mothers return about two months later.

MORE ABOUT ANTARCTICA

People have long believed there was a huge continent at the southern part of the earth. Hundreds of years ago, people called it Terra Australis.

Captain James Cook tried to find Antarctica in 1773 and again in 1774. Cook and his crew were the first sailors to cross the Antarctic Circle. He came within 121 kilometres (75 miles) of Antarctica, but he never saw land. Edward Bransfield finally discovered the main Antarctic continent on 30 January 1820.

Norwegian explorer Roald Amundsen became the first explorer to reach the South Pole, on 14 December 1911.

Due to the tilt of the Earth's axis, Antarctica receives 24 hours of sunlight each day during the summer. The sun never completely sets. The sun does not rise during the winter months. It is dark 24 hours a day.

The average temperature at South Pole Station is minus 49 degrees Celsius (minus 56 degrees Fahrenheit). Summer temperatures at McMurdo Station can be as warm as 10 degrees Celsius (50 degrees Fahrenheit).

Emperor penguins can dive more than 213 metres (700 feet) deep. They can stay under water for nearly 20 minutes.

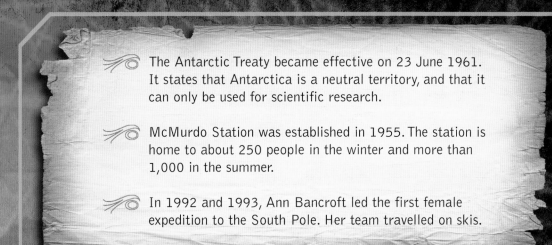

The Antarctic Treaty became effective on 23 June 1961. It states that Antarctica is a neutral territory, and that it can only be used for scientific research.

McMurdo Station was established in 1955. The station is home to about 250 people in the winter and more than 1,000 in the summer.

In 1992 and 1993, Ann Bancroft led the first female expedition to the South Pole. Her team travelled on skis.

MORE ABOUT

NAME: Isabel "Izzy" Soto
INTERESTS: People and places
BUILD: Athletic **HAIR:** Dark Brown
EYES: Brown **HEIGHT:** 1.70 m

WISP: The Worldwide Inter-dimensional Space/Time Portal developed by Max Axiom at Axiom Laboratory.

BACKSTORY: Isabel "Izzy" Soto caught the humanities bug as a little girl. Every night, her grandfather told her about his adventures exploring ancient ruins in South America. He believed people can learn a lot from other cultures and places.

Izzy's interest in cultures followed her through school and beyond. She studied history and geography. On one research trip, she discovered an ancient stone with mysterious energy. Izzy took the stone to Super Scientist Max Axiom, who determined that the stone's energy cuts across space and time. Harnessing the power of the stone, he built a device called the WISP. It opens windows to any place and any time. Although she must not use the WISP to change history, Izzy now explores events wherever and whenever they happen, solving a few mysteries along the way.

GLOSSARY

algae small plants without roots or stems that grow in water or on damp surfaces

continent one of earth's seven large land masses

crampon metal frame with pointed metal teeth that attaches to a climber's boot. Crampons give climbers secure footing on snow and ice.

crevasse deep, wide crack in a glacier or ice sheet

current movement of water in a river or an ocean

fossil fuels natural fuels formed from the remains of plants and animals. Coal, oil, and natural gas are fossil fuels.

glacier huge moving body of ice found in mountain valleys or polar regions

glaciologist scientist who studies glaciers

ice fall part of a glacier that flows more rapidly than the rest of the glacier

iceberg huge piece of ice that floats in the ocean. Icebergs break off from glaciers and ice sheets.

lichen a flat, mosslike plant that grows on trees and rocks

oceanographer scientist who studies the ocean and ocean life

SOS signal sent out to call for urgent help

terrain surface of the land

FIND OUT MORE

Books

Amundsen and Scott's Race to the South Pole, Liz Gogerly (Heinemann Library, 2008)

Arctic and Antarctic, Lorrie Mack (Dorling Kindersley, 2006)

Exploring Antarctica, Tristan Boyer Binns (Heinemann Library, 2006)

An Illustrated Atlas of South America and Antarctica, Malcolm Porter (Cherrytree Books, 2007)

On Thin Ice: Climate Change, Lynette Evans (Heinemann Library, 2009)

Internet sites

http://www.discoveringantarctica.org.uk/
This website is packed with information, pictures, videos, and activities on Antarctica.

http://www.enchantedlearning.com/school/Antarctica/
These web pages offers a look at the geography, climate, and location of Antarctica and includes profiles of Antarctic explorers, information on fossils, and more.

http://www.antarctica.ac.uk/
Click on the "Images" tab of the British Antarctic Survey website then go to the "Antarctic Picture Galleries" menu to find photos on themes from seals, penguins, and clothing, to aerial views and fossils.